Next

piano course book one

For Issie Barratt

Chester Music
(A division of Music Sales Limited)
8/9 Frith Street London W1V 5TZ

PREFACE

Congratulations to you for finishing your beginners' books – be they Chester's Easiest Piano Course or any other. You have learnt lots but there is still more to find out about! This book is the next step – providing a wide range of pieces alongside more information about music which you'll need to know.

The pieces include easy classics, modern-sounding pieces using twentieth century techniques, folk songs, ragtime and blues. As this material is more advanced, I have dispensed with accompaniments and teacher's notes. However, I hope you will continue to enjoy your practice time.

Don't forget – music is fun!

Carol Barratt

Contents of Pieces

Music processed by Seton Music Graphics Ltd
Cover design by Chloë Alexander
Printed in Great Britain by Printwise (Haverhill) Limited, Haverhill, Suffolk.

TOPICS YOU HAVE ALREADY COVERED

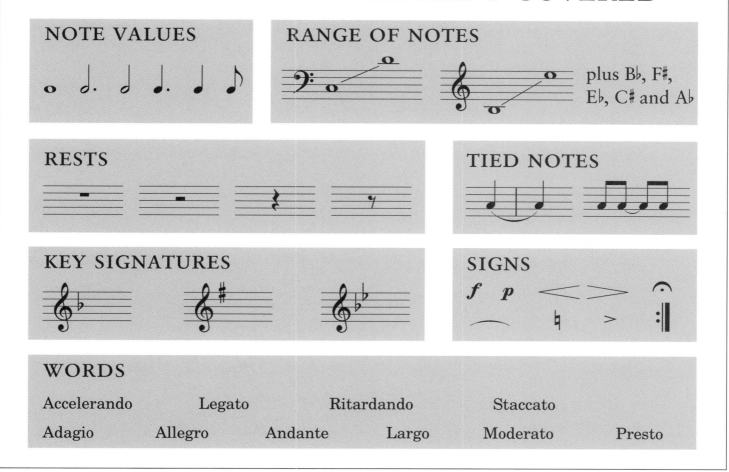

NOTE VALUES

RANGE OF NOTES

plus B♭, F♯, E♭, C♯ and A♭

RESTS

TIED NOTES

KEY SIGNATURES

SIGNS

f *p*

WORDS

Accelerando		Legato		Ritardando		Staccato	
Adagio	Allegro		Andante		Largo	Moderato	Presto

TOPICS TO BE COVERED IN THIS BOOK

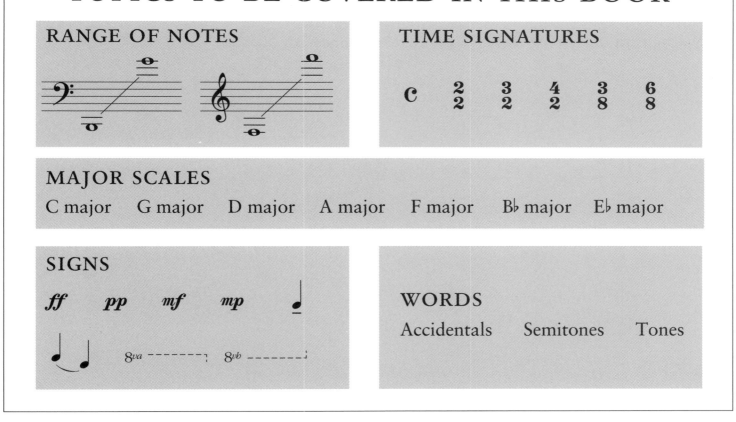

RANGE OF NOTES

TIME SIGNATURES

C $\frac{2}{2}$ $\frac{3}{2}$ $\frac{4}{2}$ $\frac{3}{8}$ $\frac{6}{8}$

MAJOR SCALES

C major   G major   D major   A major   F major   B♭ major   E♭ major

SIGNS

ff   *pp*   *mf*   *mp*

8*va* --------   8*vb* --------

WORDS

Accidentals   Semitones   Tones

QUIZ TIME

Test your knowledge of these words and signs before you start to play.

WORDS

1. *Largo* . . . .
2. *Presto* . . . .
3. *Andante* . . . .
4. *Allegro* . . . .
5. *Moderato* . . . .
6. *Adagio* . . . .
7. *Rit. (Ritardando)* . . . .
8. *Accel. (Accelerando)* . . . .
9. *Legato* . . . .
10. *Staccato* . . . .
11. *D.C. (Da capo)* . . . .
12. *Fine* . . . .

SIGNS

1. :‖ *or* ‖: :‖ . . . .
2. *p* . . . .
3. *f* . . . .
4. < . . . .
5. > . . . .
6. > . . . .
7. 𝄐 . . . .

The answers are given on page 38.

BOBBY SHAFTOE

Watch out. Some chords are tied over the bar line.
Practise the move from one position to the next,
very slowly at first but still keeping strict time.

TRADITIONAL
Arr. Carol Barratt

DRY LAND

pp (*pianissimo*) = very soft   **ff** (*fortissimo*) = very loud

CAROL BARRATT

TONES

A tone, or whole-step, is twice the distance of a semitone, or half-step.
When playing a tone you must skip a black or a white key,
as there will always be one key in between.

Play and sing
these notes:

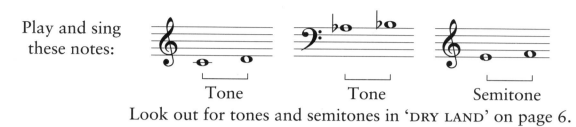

Tone   Tone   Semitone

Look out for tones and semitones in 'DRY LAND' on page 6.

MISTER FROG WENT A-COURTIN'

Allegro

AMERICAN FOLK SONG
Arr. Carol Barratt

MORE ABOUT CHORDS

When the notes of a chord are played separately,
they form broken chords and arpeggios.

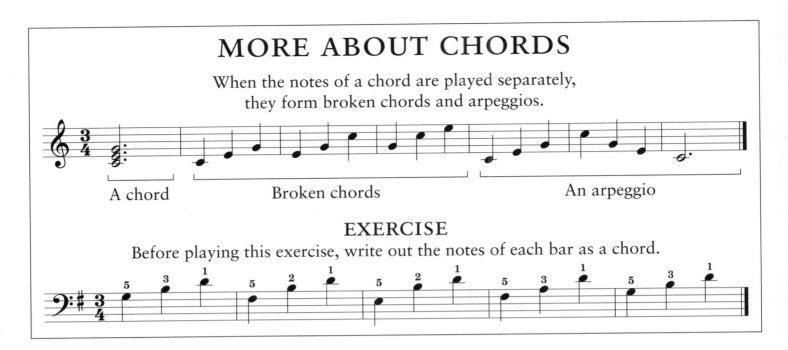

A chord   Broken chords   An arpeggio

EXERCISE

Before playing this exercise, write out the notes of each bar as a chord.

THE CHERRY TREE CAROL

Moderato

ENGLISH FOLK SONG
Arr. Carol Barratt

EXTENDING YOUR RANGE

EXERCISES

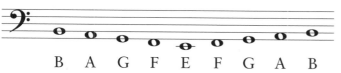

B A G F E F G A B

Play these notes after first playing Middle C.

F G A B C B A G F

Play these notes after first playing Middle C.

The extra lines needed above and below the stave are called ledger lines.

TOP AND BOTTOM

CAROL BARRATT

MINUET

(An excerpt)

This Minuet was first thought to have been written by J.S. Bach,
but it is now known to have been written by C. Petzold.

mf (*mezzo forte*) = moderately loud

mp (*mezzo piano*) = moderately soft

C. PETZOLD
(1677–1733)

Moderato

10

MINUET IN BLUE

A line over or under a note = a slight stress or pressure on the note.
It is often referred to as 'tenuto'.

CAROL BARRATT

Fairly slow

Try the Next Step Boogies, Rags and Blues Collection for more pieces like this.

FANTASY

Don't forget the two flats in the key signature.

G.P. TELEMANN (1681–1767)
Arr. Carol Barratt

LES CINQ DOIGTS

Watch out. Both hands play in the 𝄞 clef.
Look at the left hand in bars 13–20. The note G is held on with
for a ♩ as fingers 2, 3, 4, 5 play the ♫ ♫ underneath.
This is called part-playing: i.e. two parts are played by one hand.

I. STRAVINSKY
(1882–1971)

NOW IT'S YOUR TURN!

Compose a left hand part for the tune below. Try using these as broken chords:

Don't forget to add a title, expression marks and your name:

MORE ABOUT TIME SIGNATURES

A common way of writing $\frac{4}{4}$ is 𝄴

𝄴 stands for common time

2 stands for minim (half-note) as

4 stands for crotchet (quarter-note) as

8 stands for quaver (eighth-note) as

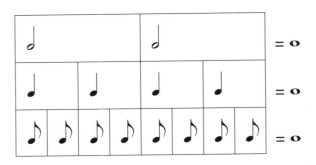

THE SEAGULL

Each beat is a minim

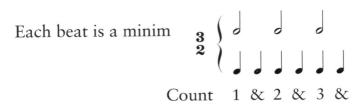

Count   1 & 2 & 3 &

Adagio

IRISH FOLK SONG
Arr. Carol Barratt

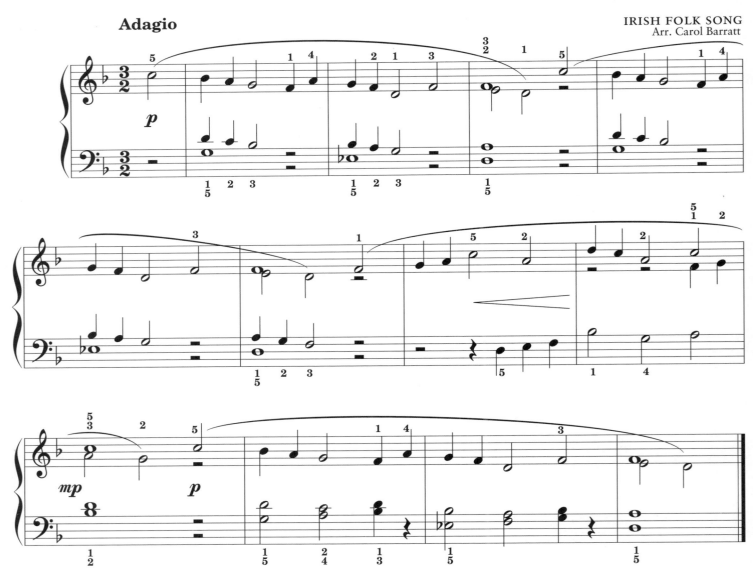

14

EXERCISES

GET COUNTING!

Moderato

CAROL BARRATT

SLURS

A slur is a curved line.

This line is like an umbrella covering two or more notes and indicates that these notes are to be played smoothly (*legato*). Think of a slur as a short phrase.

TWO-NOTE SLURS
Follow these three steps:
1. As you play the first note, the hand and wrist are level.
2. As you approach the second note, the wrist is raised.
3. As you play the second note, the hand is lifted from the keyboard.

THREE-NOTE SLURS
This time raise the wrist as you approach the **third** note, lifting the hand off as you play it.

EXERCISE
Play it as written and then with the left hand starting on C below middle C.

PASSEPIED

(A lively dance)

G.F. HANDEL
(1685-1759)

16

STUDY IN BLACK AND WHITE

Moderato

CAROL BARRATT

THINGS TO DO

1. First find some music manuscript paper!
(Failing that, use page 39 of this book)

2. Compose a tune.
Write a tune to fit the rhythm given below.

Don't forget to add phrase marks.

3. Change around
Re-write this exercise putting rests in place of notes,
and notes (on any line or space) in place of rests.

4. Finding the time
Write in the missing time signatures.

5. In number 4 above, write T (for tone) or S (for semitone) next to the brackets.

SUPERSTUDY

Presto (eventually!)

CAROL BARRATT

19

ANOTHER TIME SIGNATURE $\frac{6}{8}$

There are two main ♩. beats in each bar and each of the two beats is divided into three ♪'s

Think of $\frac{6}{8}$ as $\frac{2}{♩.}$

Count six at first to make it easy, putting a strong accent on the first count and a weaker accent on the fourth.

ONE two three FOUR five six

Play these examples counting (i) six ♪'s per bar (ii) two ♩.'s per bar

Count (i)   1   2   3   4   5   6   1   2   3   4 - 5 - 6
Count (ii) 1   2   1   2

Count (i)   1 - 2 - 3   4 - 5 - 6   1 - 2 - 3   4 - 5 - 6
Count (ii) 1   2   1   2

Count (i)   1 - 2   3   4 - 5   6   1 - 2   3   4 - 5 - 6
Count (ii) 1   2   1   2

𝄾. = ♩. rest

The value of a whole bar = ♩. ♩. or 𝅗𝅥.

PLANTING THE CABBAGE

FRENCH FOLK SONG
Arr. Carol Barratt

COMPLETE THESE FOUR BARS

Fill in the bars below, adding a tune to the suggested rhythm.
The pitch of the first and fourth quavers is given.

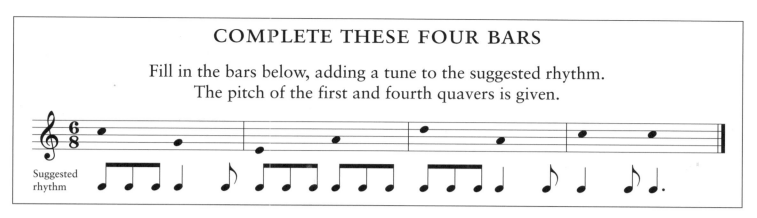

Suggested rhythm

TWO ARRANGEMENTS OF THE SAME PIECE

a. With two ♩. beats (⁶₈)   b. With two ♩ beats (²₄)

IF ALL THE WORLD WERE PAPER

ENGLISH FOLK SONG
Arr. Carol Barratt

GIGUE

WALTZ

22

HERBERT'S HORNPIPE

CAROL BARRATT

MAJOR SCALES

C MAJOR AND G MAJOR

A scale is a "musical ladder" on which most tunes are built.
The ladder has eight notes placed in alphabetical order.

THE MAJOR SCALE

The pattern of every major scale is like C major,
as the tones and semitones are always arranged as follows:

C major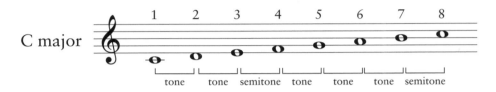

There are semitones between notes 3 and 4, and between notes 7 and 8.
In order to keep to this pattern of tones and semitones, ♯s and ♭s are
needed in all the other major scales.
From now on, tone = T and semitone =S.

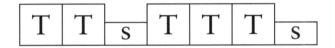

Build up the major scale starting on G, and as scales are named by
the note that starts off the pattern, this will be called G major.

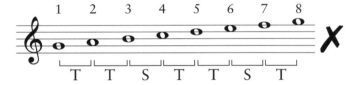 

WRONG – The last two notes
don't fit the pattern

RIGHT – The seventh note must
be raised a semitone to
keep the major scale pattern.

THE KEY SIGNATURE OF G MAJOR

 When the notes of a piece of music are taken from the scale of G major, the
piece is said to be in the key of G major, and the key signature is called the
key signature of G major. Look at the "Minuet" on page 10.

AN ACCIDENTAL

Look at "Dry Land" on page 6. This is in the key of G major. The C♯ in bar 4
and bar 16 is an accidental – any sign (♯♭ or ♮) that is not in the key signature
but is put next to a note, is called an accidental.

PLAYING SCALES

The eight notes can be played without a break by turning the thumb <u>under</u> the hands.

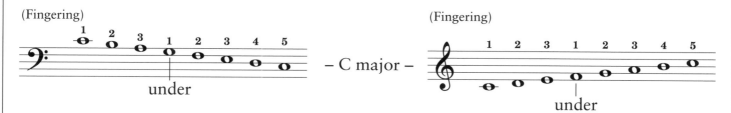

– C major –

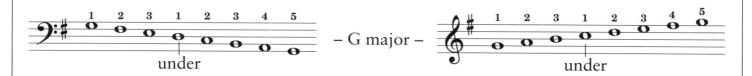

– G major –

If you go the opposite way to the previous examples, the hands go <u>over</u> the thumbs

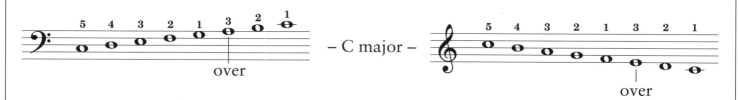

– C major –

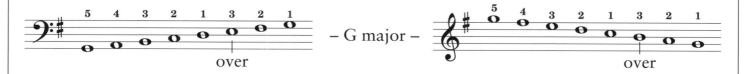

– G major –

Now play C major and G major with both hands in both directions.

C MAJOR

G MAJOR

This time, for a change, the hands start an octave apart.

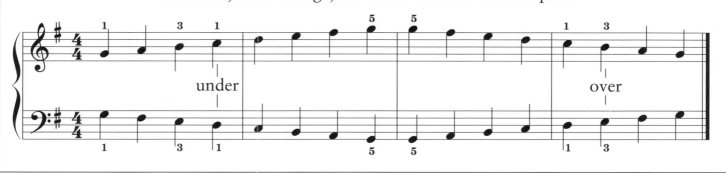

EXERCISES

For the thumbs.

TURNING POINT

Allegro

CAROL BARRATT

ONE TUNE – TWO KEYS

"On a Monday Morning" is the same piece of music as "On a Friday Morning",
but the first is in C major and the second is in G major five notes higher.
Can you point out the accidentals?

ON A MONDAY MORNING . . .

POLISH FOLK SONG
Arr. Carol Barratt

. . . ON A FRIDAY MORNING

Watch out. The *p*'s and *f*'s are in different places.

OCTAVE SIGNS

8va - - - - - - - ⌐

This sign tells you to play the note or notes an octave <u>higher</u> than written.

8vb - - - - - - ⌐

This sign tells you to play the note or notes an octave <u>lower</u> than written.

CAROL'S CAKEWALK

(A ragtime dance)

CAROL BARRATT

28

MORE NOTES

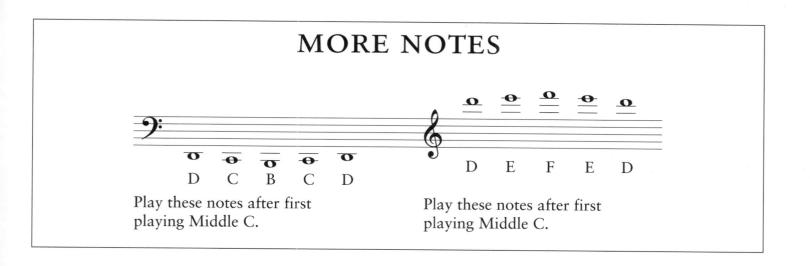

D C B C D

Play these notes after first
playing Middle C.

D E F E D

Play these notes after first
playing Middle C.

U.F.O.'S

For an eerie and blurred effect, hold the sustaining
pedal down throughout the entire piece.

CAROL BARRATT

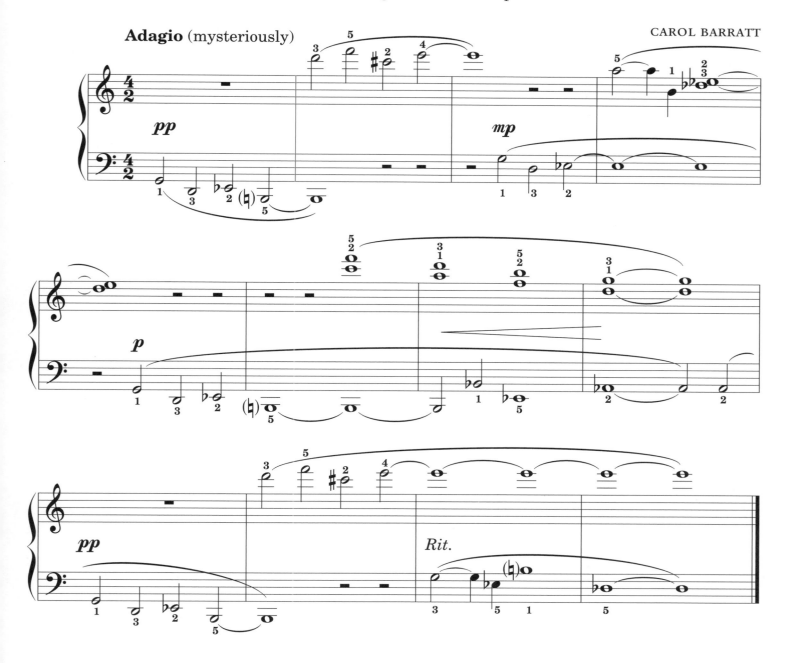

29

MORE MAJOR SCALES

Complete the scales given below, adding sharps or flats when necessary. Check that you have **one** of each letter-name (except for note number 8 which has the same letter-name as note number 1). Remember the pattern TTSTTTS of the major scale.

EXERCISES

F major has been completed for you. Play them after you have completed them.

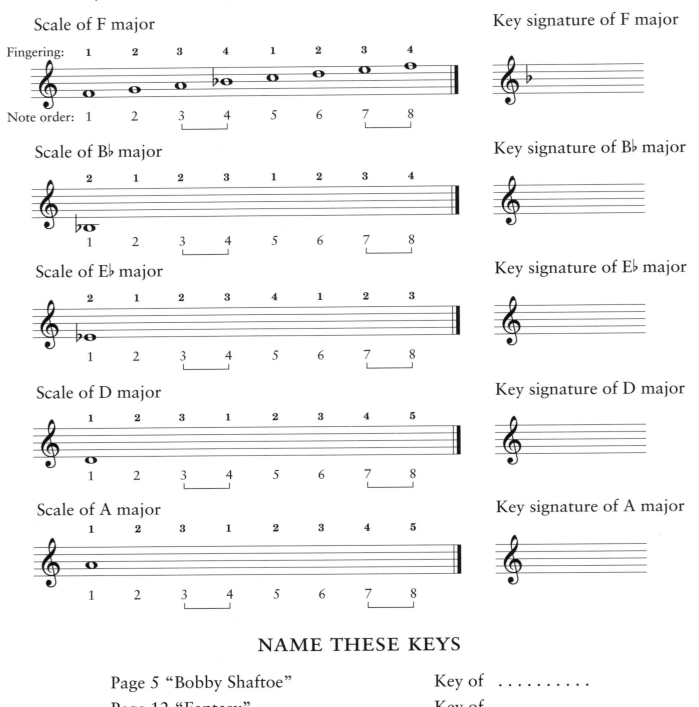

NAME THESE KEYS

Page 5 "Bobby Shaftoe"   Key of . . . .

Page 12 "Fantasy"   Key of . . . .

Page 31 "Rig-a-Jig-Jig"   Key of . . . .

Page 32 "German Dance"   Key of . . . .

Page 33 "Hop, Step & Jump"   Key of . . . .

RIG-A-JIG-JIG

ENGLISH FOLK SONG
Arr. Carol Barratt

OLD NOTES ON NEW LEDGER LINES

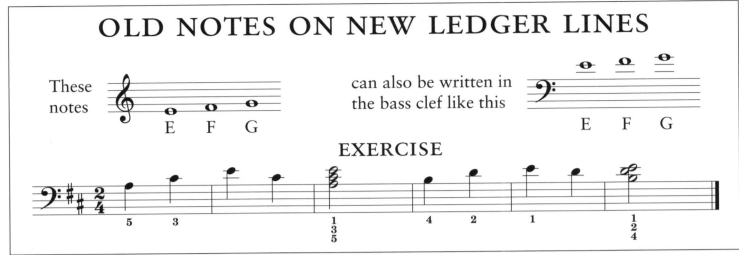

GERMAN DANCE

F.J. HAYDN
(1732–1809)

32

OLD NOTES ON NEW LEDGER LINES

These notes  can also be written in the treble clef like this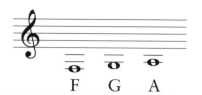

HOP, STEP & JUMP

Moderato

CAROL BARRATT

TWO HANDS – TWO KEYS

The piece below is in two keys at the same time.
The right hand is in E♭ major and the left hand is in G major.
To make the piece easier to read, accidentals are used instead of key signatures.
Don't forget that each beat is a minim (half note).

CAROL BARRATT

Adagio

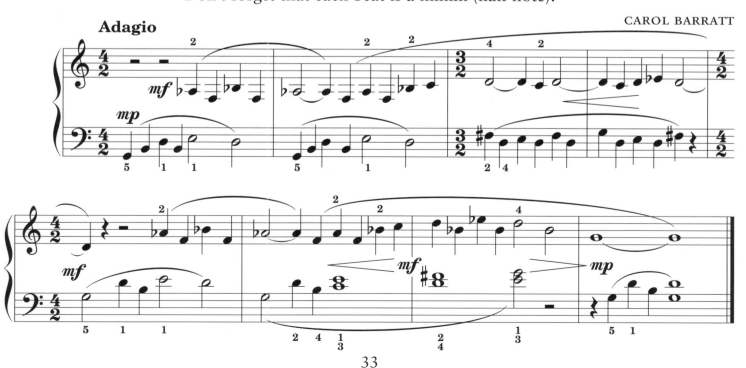

33

EXERCISE

Don't forget to hold on to the minims (half-notes) in bars 1, 3, 5 and 6.

LEEZIE LINDSAY

SCOTTISH FOLK SONG
Arr. Carol Barratt

Moderato

34

SOME TRICKY RHYTHMS

Tap out the following examples:

Look out for (c) and (d) on page 37.

FIDGETY DIGITS

CAROL BARRATT

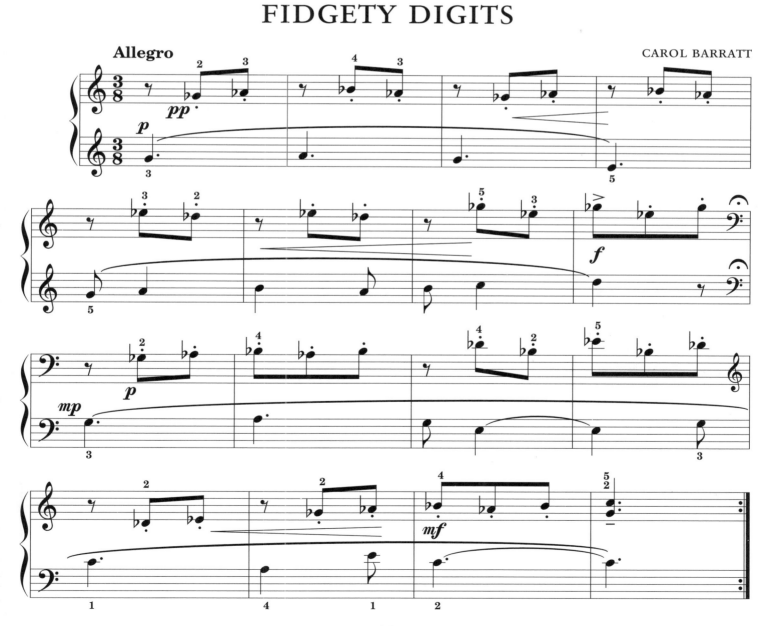

DUET

A SHORT SHUFFLE

Second player

CAROL BARRATT

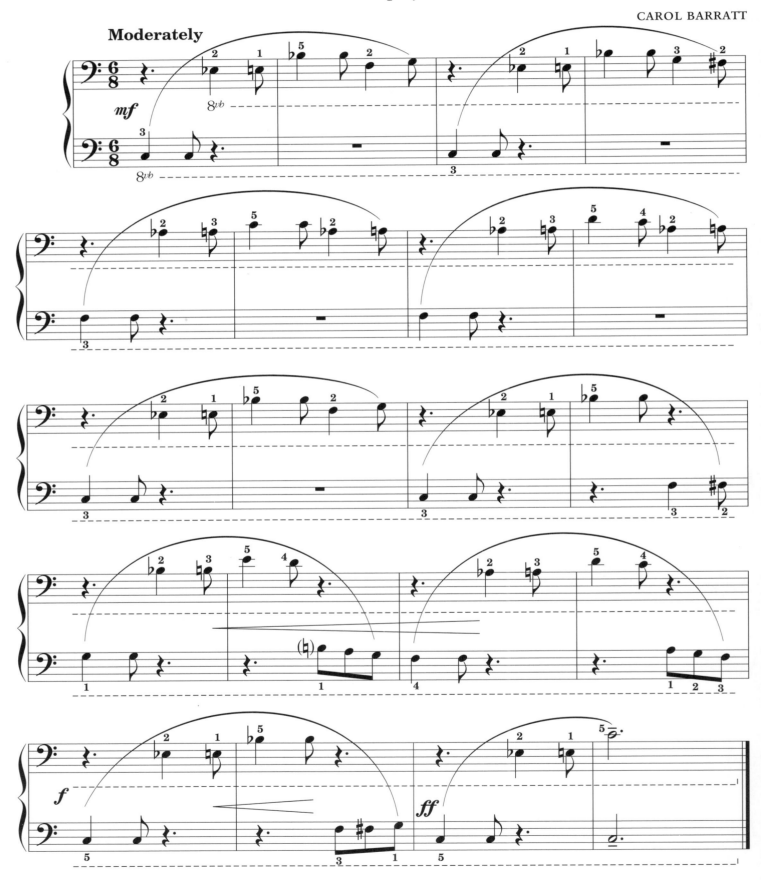

DUET

A SHORT SHUFFLE

First player

Moderately

CAROL BARRATT

ANSWERS TO QUIZ (PAGE 4)

WORDS

1. *Largo* = very slow
2. *Presto* = very fast
3. *Andante* = fairly slow
4. *Allegro* = fast
5. *Moderato* = moderately
6. *Adagio* = slow
7. *Rit.* (*Ritardando*) = slow down
8. *Accel.* (*Accelerando*) = get faster
9. *Legato* = playing smoothly
10. *Staccato* = short crisp notes. A dot above or below a note tells you when to play staccato
11. *D.C.* (*Da capo*) = go back to the beginning
12. *Fine* = the end

SIGNS

1. :‖ or ‖: :‖ = repeat
2. *p* (*piano*) = soft
3. *f* (*forte*) = loud
4. ＜ = getting gradually louder
5. ＞ = getting gradually softer
6. > = accent. The notes are played with extra force
7. ⌢ = pause. The notes are held on for longer than their value

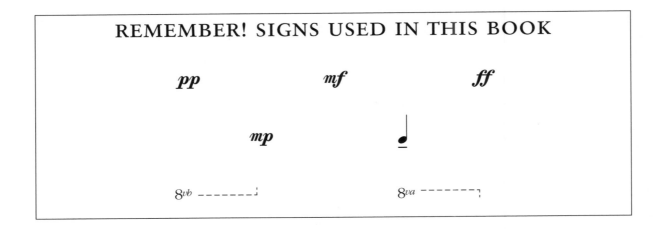

REMEMBER! SIGNS USED IN THIS BOOK

pp   *mf*   *ff*

mp   ♩

8vb - - - - - - -⌐   *8va - - - - - - -⌐*

Have you tried...

Next Step
Boogies, Rags and Blues
Collection

This progressive collection of boogies, rags and blues will help develop a strong sense of rhythm as well as an appreciation of an important area of twentieth century music.

Written by Carol Barratt specifically for intermediate standard players.

Ideal supplementary material for use alongside the Next Step Piano Course Books 1 & 2.

Next Step
Piano Allsorts Collection

This progressively graded collection includes a wealth of repertoire ranging from the 17th to the 20th centuries – from Bach to the blues.

Designed for intermediate players and ideal as supplementary material to the Next Step Piano Course Book 2.

Including pieces by Mozart, Joplin, Franck, Corelli, JS Bach, Schubert, Grieg, Nielsen, Diabelli, Chopin, von Dittersdorf, Handel, Kabalevsky, Prokofiev, Haydn, Glinka and Beethoven, plus folk songs from around the world and original works by Carol Barratt.

Developed by Carol Barratt, author of the most popular and successful piano tutors, the Next Step Piano Course is a logical progression for anyone who has been playing for one year upwards.

Chester Music
(A division of Music Sales Limited)
Exclusive distributors:
Music Sales Limited, Newmarket Road, Bury St Edmunds, Suffolk IP33 3YB.